The Adventures of Yat and Dat

WHAT'S COOKIN'?

Written by Nancy Parker · Illustrated by Spencer Bradford

AMP&RSAND, INC.

Chicago · New Orleans

ISBN 978-145070619-3

Design
David Robson, Robson Design

Published by
AMPERSAND, INC.
1050 North State Street
Chicago, Illinois 60610

———

203 Finland Place
New Orleans, Louisiana 70131

———

www.ampersandworks.com

———

Printed in Canada

———————— ⚜ ————————

DEDICATED TO:

My parents, PATSY AND WILLIAM PARKER, for instilling in me at an early age
the magic found in books, and the limitless possibilities in life.
My husband, GLYNN, and our children, PARKER, PIPER AND PIERCE,
for inspiring me every day.

The patients, families, doctors and staff of
ST. JUDE CHILDREN'S RESEARCH HOSPITAL in Memphis, Tennessee

AND TO THE GREAT CHEFS OF NEW ORLEANS
WHO MOTIVATED YAT AND DAT:

MICHELLE McRANEY, Executive Chef, *Mr. B's Bistro*
MICHAEL REGUA, Executive Chef, *Antoine's Restaurant*
LAZONE RANDOLPH, Executive Chef, *Brennan's*
LEAH CHASE, World Famous Chef, *Dookey Chase's*
GERALD "SHORTROUND" PEIRCE, Top Chef, *The Camellia Grill*
DREXTIAL CARTER, Executive Chef, *The Praline Connection*
DAVID WOODWARD, Executive Chef, *Drago's Seafood Restaurant*
BRIAN LANDRY, Executive Chef, *Galatoire's Restaurant*
EMERIL LAGASSE, Executive Chef and Proprietor, *Emeril's New Orleans*

———————— ⚜ ————————

Yat and Dat are in their tree
Above the Faubourg Marigny.

And they're in a sassy mood,
Tired of scraps and seeds for food.

"Eating like birds just isn't fair
When culinary masterpieces are everywhere!"

"Yes, indeed, Dat! Yeah — you right!
Let's make our own masterpiece tonight."

In a big washtub they'd mix with care
The very, very best of New Orleans fare.

"Let's go!" Dat's hunger made him queasy.
Off they flew around the Big Easy.

"BBQ Shrimp!" Yat at once agrees.
They hover at the door of the famous Mr. B's.

When they sail in, a waitress starts to shriek.
Yat locks a shrimp securely in her beak.

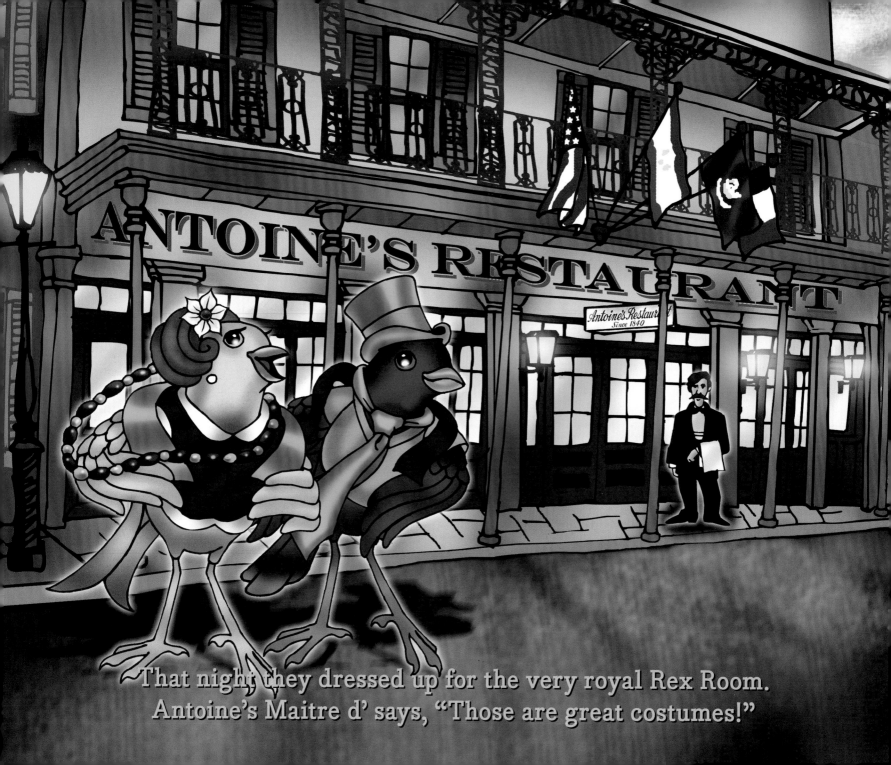

That night they dressed up for the very royal Rex Room.
Antoine's Maitre d' says, "Those are great costumes!"

Dat could not resist the famous speckled trout.
"Now dat's *exactly* what I'm talkin' about!"

The next day they make their way around the old French Quarter.
And stop at Jackson Square to get a drink of water.

"She's gonna drop dat take-out box!" says Dat, spellbound.
And then a Brennan's masterpiece tumbles to the ground.

Dat brings his haul to the bubbling pot.
Yat adds some Beignets. "They're pipin' hot!"

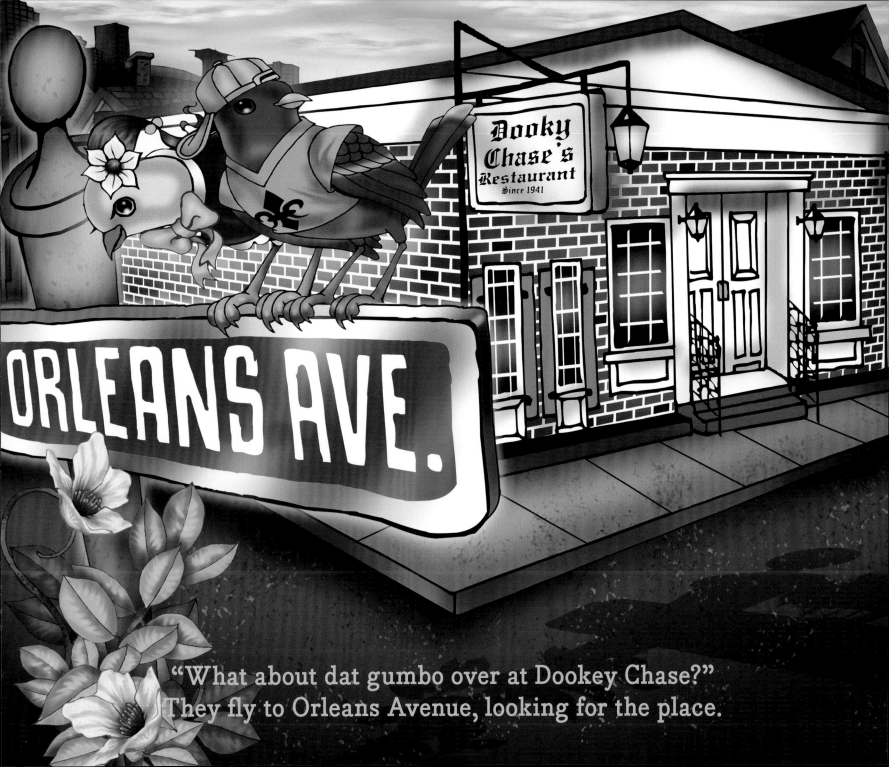

"What about dat gumbo over at Dookey Chase?"
They fly to Orleans Avenue, looking for the place.

The tub is filling up now, and it's far from run-of-the-mill.
Dat grabs a chili-cheese omelet from Uptown's Camellia Grill.

Then they smell some red beans cooking on a lady's stove.
She is selling plates of them, right there in Hollygrove.

"The Praline Connection!" says Yat. "Dat etouffee can't be beat."
They snagged a crawfish for the pot right there on Frenchman Street!

"Let's add some oysters from dat big ol' fire at Drago's!"
And just how they did *that*, nobody really knows.

"I think we got enough", Yat firmly said.
But it wouldn't be New Orleans without some good French bread.

Off they go to Galatoire's. Dat really gets to work.
The bona fide, bird-i-fied New Orleans Yat gives him a great big CHIRP!

Back in the Marigny it's time to stir the pot.
Yat picks up a stick and mixes the foaming lot.

One taste and Dat *gags!* He cannot tell a lie.
"Dis is just like river water!" He really wants to *cry!*

"Yuck! Dis stuff is awful. It's really, *really* bad!"
All that work for nothing! They were feeling very sad.

With the mess still in the washtub they fly up to their tree
And ponder for a moment what their next move might be.

They were so tired, they could barely move at all,
But Yat and Dat admitted that they had had a ball.

"Let's leave it to da chefs, dey really know what's cookin'.
And we can eat a lot when no one's really lookin'."

And so from that day on Yat and Dat agreed to dine
On famous New Orleans leftovers…and that would be just fine!

YAT AND DAT EXPLAIN

New Orleans La Nouvelle-Orléans was founded in 1718 by the French Mississippi Company and was named for Philippe d'Orléans, Duke of Orléans and Regent of France.

The Big Easy Legend is that jazz and blues musicians gave New Orleans this nickname over 100 years ago because it was so easy for musicians to make a living there.

Faubourg Marigny is a neighborhood in New Orleans laid out in the early 1800s by Bernard X. P. de Marigny de Mandeville on land that had been his family's plantation.

French Quarter also known as the Vieux Carré, is the oldest neighborhood in New Orleans and the site of the city's first settlers.

Jackson Square Originally known as Place d'Armes, this historic park in the French Quarter was renamed Jackson Square in honor of Andrew Jackson who successfully fought the British in the War of 1812. The statue of Jackson was sculpted by Clark Mills.

Uptown is the area upriver from Canal Street, which was the dividing line between "Uptown" and the historic "Downtown" of New Orleans in the 19th century. British descendents developed homes, mansions and businesses Uptown and the descendents of French and Spanish ancestors remained Downtown, in the old French Quarter. The terms refer to the direction of the flow of the Mississippi River.

Hollygrove is a New Orleans neighborhood located in the city's 17th Ward.

❧

Mr. B's Bistro is a comfortable and relaxed French Quarter spot specializing in contemporary Creole cooking. It was among five nationwide nominees for the James Beard MasterCard Outstanding Service Award in 1994 and 1995, winner of the Ivy Award and Fine Dining Hall of Fame Award in 1988.

Antoine's is the oldest family-run restaurant in the U.S., established in 1840. One of its dining rooms, The Rex Room, is dedicated to "The Krewe of Rex" whose monarch reigns as the King of Mardi Gras.

Brennan's Owen Edward Brennan founded this culinary phenomenon in 1946. The restaurant is famous for breakfast, offering some of the world's most imaginative dishes. At breakfast or dinner, a finale of Bananas Foster, Brennan's world-famous creation, is a must. This dessert is the most requested item on the menu.

Café Du Monde Established in 1862 in the New Orleans French Market, this traditional coffee shop offers dark roasted coffee and chicory, served black or au lait (half coffee, half hot milk) along with beignets. It is open 24 hours a day every day except Christmas.

Dooky Chase's was once owned by renowned chef Leah Chase's in-laws. She started working in the restaurant in the 1950s and has since converted the menu to her own Creole recipes. African-American art from her extensive collection is a key element of Dooky Chase's décor.

The Camellia Grill This landmark on S. Carrollton Avenue at Riverbend opened in 1946. It is famous for over-stuffed omelettes and diner classics.

The Praline Connection began as a home delivery service for career women who were too busy to cook. Cecil Kaigler and Curtis Moore opened TPC in 1990, specializing in "down home" Cajun-creole style soul food. They make pralines every day the old fashioned way.

Drago's Seafood Restaurant Opened in 1970 by Klara and Drago Cvitanovich, Drago's continues a tradition of great dining provided by the close-knit Croatian community of New Orleans. It is the realization of a dream and the beginning of what has become one of the city's institutions.

Galatoire's Restaurant Time-honored customs characterize this monument to authentic French Creole cuisine. For over 100 years, theirs has been a tradition of serving dishes at a level that raises them to an art form. Steady patrons have said that the beauty of Galatoire's is that nothing ever changes.

Emeril's New Orleans In 1990, Emeril Lagasse, famous cookbook writer, TV and radio chef, opened this award-winning restaurant in the Warehouse District, followed by NOLA Restaurant in the French Quarter and Emeril's Delmonico in the historic Garden District. He is now chef-proprietor of 12 restaurants in New Orleans, Las Vegas, Orlando, Miami, Gulfport and Bethlehem, PA.

❧

Beignet (ben-yeah) a French donut made of deep-fried dough sprinkled with confectioner's sugar.

Etouffee (eh-too-fay) thicker than gumbo, this Louisiana dish is made with crawfish, shrimp or crabmeat cooked in a base of dark roux, onions, green peppers and celery then seasoned with cayenne pepper, garlic and salt. It is easy to make and is usually served over rice.

BBQ Shrimp At Mr. B's Bistro, BBQ Shrimp means shrimp sautéed in many sticks of butter and Worcestershire Sauce. The shrimp are cooked and served in the shell, so it's best not to dig in unless you are wearing a bib.

Red Beans is an old Creole dish traditionally made on Mondays using the ham bone left over from Sunday dinner. Red beans, bell pepper, onion, celery, spices and the ham bone are simmered on the stove for hours then served over white rice. The custom of making red beans and rice every Monday came from the time when women spent hours on end scrubbing clothes on washday which happened to be Monday.

Speckled Trout is actually known as a spotted sea trout but either way, it is not a trout at all. The speckled trout is a member of the drum family and is found in the southern United States.

Gumbo The name comes from the African plant, okingumbo, which is the source of okra, a key ingredient of this original Louisiana soup. To make it, you start with a roux, then add the "holy trinity" of celery, bell peppers and onion along with meat or seafood. It is traditionally served over rice.

"BAM!" is a favorite expression of renowned Chef, Emeril Lagasse. Every now and then, he also "kicks it up a notch!"

Find the famous restaurants that Yat and Dat visited.

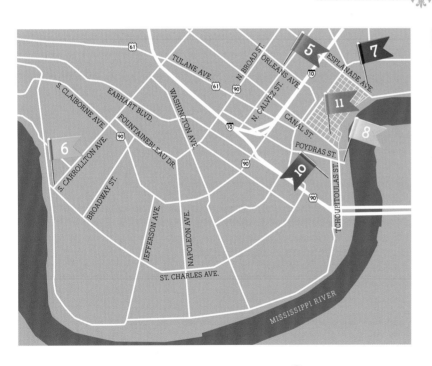

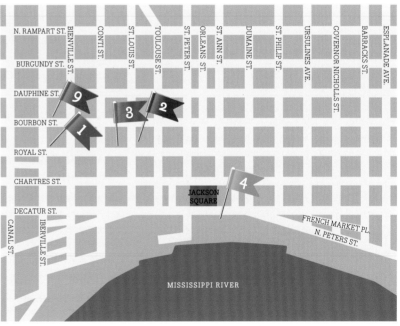

① *Mr. B's Bistro Restaurant* 201 Royal Street

② *Antoine's Restaurant* 713 Saint Louis Street

③ *Brennan's Restaurant* 417 Royal Street

④ *Cafe Du Monde Coffee Stand* 800 Decatur Street

⑤ *Dooky Chase Restaurant* 2301 Orleans Avenue

⑥ *Camellia Grill* 626 South Carrollton Avenue

⑦ *Praline Connection* 542 Frenchmen Street

⑧ *Drago's Seafood Restaurant* 2 Poydras Street

⑨ *Galatoire's* 209 Bourbon Street

⑩ *Emeril's New Orleans* 800 Tchoupitoulas Street

⑪ French Quarter *See detail map at right*